Our Baby Throws Things

Bill Gillham

Illustrated by Margaret Chamberlain

Methuen Children's Books

Our baby throws things.

He throws his rabbit,

and he throws his bottle.

He throws the covers
out of his cot.

Oops!

Sometimes he throws himself!

When Dad takes him
for a walk,

he throws things out
of the pram.

He thinks it's a game!

Here is our baby
outside the supermarket.

What *is* he doing?

He's found the shopping bag!

Throw out the toilet rolls.

Throw out the eggs.

Bananas taste funny
with the peel on.

Throw them out too!

What's that noise?

A man's robbed the bank!

Mind those bananas –
and eggs and toilet rolls!

Crash!

"Our baby's caught
the robber!" said Dad.

Because he throws things!

How to pair read

1 Sit the child next to you, so that you can both see the book.

2 Tell the child you are *both* going to read the story *at the same time*. To begin with the child will be hesitant: adjust your speed so that you are reading almost simultaneously, *pointing to the words* as you go.

3 If the child makes a mistake, repeat the correct word but *keep going* so that fluency is maintained.

4 Gradually increase your speed once you and the child are reading together.

5 As the child becomes more confident, lower your voice and, progressively, try dropping out altogether.

6 If the child stumbles or gets stuck, give the correct word and continue 'pair-reading' to support fluency, dropping out again quite quickly.

7 Read the story *right through* once a day but not more than twice, so that it stays fresh.

8 After about 5–8 readings the child will usually be reading the book independently.

In its original form paired reading was first devised by Roger Morgan and Elizabeth Lyon, and described in a paper published in the Journal of Child Psychology and Psychiatry (1979).

First published in Great Britain in 1986
by Methuen Children's Books Ltd, 11 New Fetter Lane, London EC4P 4EE
Text copyright © 1986 Bill Gillham. Illustrations copyright © 1986 Margaret Chamberlain
Printed in Great Britain ISBN 0 416 95810 9